P9-CLS-579
Mowgli
Ranjan
Shanti
Here's a WILD
place for my name.
Smolen

Published by Scholastic Inc.,
90 Old Sherman Turnpike, Danbury, Connecticut 06816.

For information regarding permission, write to:
Disney Licensed Publishing, 114 Fifth Avenue,
New York, New York 10011.

ISBN 0-7172-6751-2

Printed in the U.S.A.
First printing, October 2006

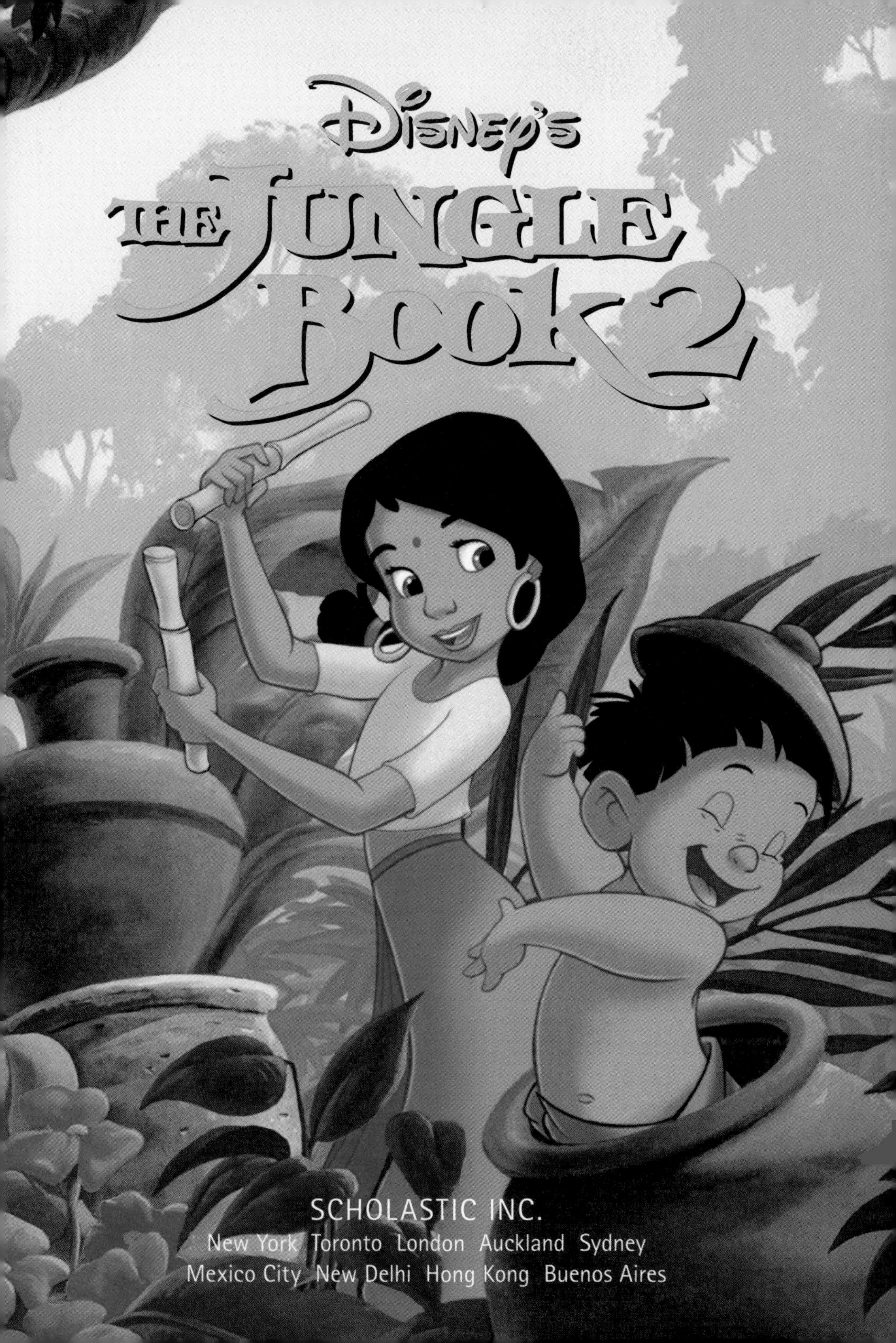

SCHOLASTIC INC.
New York Toronto London Auckland Sydney
Mexico City New Delhi Hong Kong Buenos Aires

Mowgli loved the jungle. It was home to him and his best friends, Baloo the friendly bear and Bagheera the panther.

But when Shere Khan the tiger started stalking Mowgli, his friends decided the boy should live in the Man-village. Mowgli hadn't wanted to go . . . until he saw a pretty girl named Shanti.

Since that day, Mowgli had been living in the Man-village with a boy named Ranjan and his family.

One morning, Ranjan pounced on Mowgli. "*ROOAARH!*" Ranjan shouted. "Come on, Mowgli, wake up!" Ranjan was excited. He and Mowgli had special plans for the morning.

Shouting happily, the two boys left the house.

Ranjan's father called after them, "Remember, don't cross the river!" Then he said to his wife, "You can take the boy out of the jungle . . . "

"But you can't take the jungle out of the boy," she added.

Mowgli and Ranjan crept down to the river where Shanti was fetching water.

Mowgli sidled up to her. "Yesterday I saw tiger tracks right here!" he whispered.

Shanti looked around nervously. Suddenly she heard a rustling in the bushes, then a loud *ROOOAARRR*!

"*YAAAHHH!*" screamed Shanti. She glared at the two boys when she realized they were teasing her.

Mowgli showed Ranjan a jungle trick. He squeezed the peel off a banana and popped the fruit into Ranjan's mouth.

"That's a good trick," Ranjan said.

Shanti wasn't impressed. She tossed a mango up in the air, and it caught on a sharp branch. The fruit twirled around, and the peeled mango fell into her hand.

"Wow!" Ranjan said. "That's a neater trick!"

Not to be outdone, Mowgli tried to show the village children how to listen to the jungle beat. Without thinking, he started to lead them into the jungle.

Shanti panicked. "Wait—stop!" she shouted. "You're crossing the river. It's too dangerous!"

Ranjan's father heard Shanti and ran to the river. "Children!" he yelled. "Come inside this instant! Mowgli," he added, "that includes you."

"You put everyone in danger," Ranjan's father scolded Mowgli. Wanting Mowgli to remember this lesson, Ranjan's father said, "You are confined to your room without dinner."

"Oh, Baloo . . ." Mowgli said later, staring at the jungle through his window. He really missed his old friend.

And Baloo missed Mowgli, too, and had even made a pretend Man-cub out of a coconut. But it was no use. "You just ain't Mowgli," Baloo told the coconut.

"Poor fellow," said Bagheera. The panther went to comfort Baloo, but he had already left. Realizing that his friend had probably gone to see Mowgli, Bagheera hurried to stop Baloo.

And they weren't the only ones heading for the Man-village. Shere Khan was also on his way!

In the village, Mowgli heard something outside his window. He hopped out to investigate.

"Baloo!" gasped Mowgli.

"Hi, kid!" said Baloo. "Mind if I drop in?"

Mowgli jumped into his old friend's arms. "Boy am I glad to see you!" announced Mowgli.

Shanti was also sneaking out to see Mowgli. She wanted to apologize for getting him into trouble.

She didn't know Shere Khan was looking for Mowgli, too.

Then Shanti saw Baloo and Mowgli. She didn't know they were friends.

"There's a wild animal in the village!" cried Shanti.

"Wild animal—where?" said Baloo, not thinking of himself as a wild animal. He grabbed Mowgli and ran.

The villagers heard Shanti and rushed out to fight the wild animal. They didn't see Baloo. But they did see Shere Khan!

"Oh, my goodness, there he is!" cried Ranjan's mother, pointing at the tiger.

Shanti tried to tell everyone that it was a bear that had kidnapped Mowgli.

But the villagers were already racing after Shere Khan.

Because the villagers were chasing the tiger into the jungle, Shanti decided to try to save Mowgli herself. She ran into the jungle, unaware that Ranjan was following her.

And Mowgli didn't know that Shanti was following him.

"That village is terrible," said Mowgli. "All you ever hear is rules, rules, rules, and work, work, work."

"Oh, man, I'm tired just listening to it," said Baloo.

"I don't want to talk about it," Mowgli declared to Baloo, "especially Shanti."

But then Mowgli proceeded to tell Baloo all about Shanti. "She thinks the jungle is a scary place," the boy added.

"Where did she get that crazy idea?" Baloo wondered.

Meanwhile, Shanti was learning that the jungle *was* a scary place for a lost young girl. As she searched for Mowgli, Shanti bumped right into Kaa the python.

Kaa stared into her eyes. "Excussse me," hissed Kaa. "Are you hungry? I'm ssstarved."

Shanti looked into Kaa's hypnotizing eyes.

Suddenly little Ranjan dragged Shanti away from Kaa. "Bad snake. Bad, bad, bad snake!" cried Ranjan, as he hit Kaa on the head with a branch.

Kaa slithered away, and Ranjan and Shanti kept looking for Mowgli together.

In another part of the jungle, Mowgli was showing Baloo the mango trick he had learned.

"Hey, hey, not bad!" exclaimed Baloo. "Where did ya learn that?"

"Shanti showed me," said Mowgli. Oops! Mowgli hadn't meant to talk about Shanti again.

Just then Bagheera showed up. Baloo hid Mowgli from Bagheera.

"Man is in the jungle!" said the panther, who had heard the villagers calling for the children.

"They're searching for Mowgli. I thought that perhaps you have seen the boy?" Bagheera asked.

"Me? No, naw," lied Baloo.

After Bagheera left, Mowgli cried, "Wow! The whole village is looking for me? I wonder if Shanti is with them."

"Shanti?" said Baloo. "Now, Mowgli, what if that girl tracks us down?"

"Then you're gonna have to scare her!" said Mowgli.

Baloo practiced. He took a deep breath and let out a loud *ROAR*!

"Yeah, man!" cried Mowgli. "That was great!"

But just to be safe, Baloo decided to take Mowgli to a place downriver.

Not long after they left, Shanti and Ranjan arrived, and Shanti found the mango peel on the ground. Now she knew that Mowgli had been there. "But where is he now?" Shanti was worried.

She didn't know Baloo had taken Mowgli to an ancient temple where all the animals were dancing around the ruins. Mowgli and Baloo joined the fun.

"They don't swing out like that in your Man-village, now do they, kid?" asked a monkey.

"Let me lay it out for you," interrupted Baloo. "Everybody works and nobody plays. They've got nothing but rules."

Mowgli felt guilty. The village wasn't as bad as he had described it to Baloo. Mowgli even missed the village—a bit. Feeling alone, he quietly wandered off.

Mowgli hopped onto a branch to think. He began to sing a song.

As Shanti carried Ranjan through the jungle, she heard Mowgli singing. Shanti followed the sound.

"Mowgli!" called Shanti excitedly.

Mowgli was so startled that he fell out of the tree. "What are you doing out here?" he asked.

"We came to save you from that wild bear," Shanti explained.

Just then Baloo, who had been looking for Mowgli, spotted Shanti. Not wanting Shanti to take Mowgli back to the village, the bear did exactly what Mowgli had told him to do. Baloo tried to scare her and let loose with a mighty *ROAR*!

Reacting quickly, Shanti punched Baloo.

"Ow!" yelled Baloo.

Mowgli stopped Shanti from swinging again.

"But he's attacking us," said a confused Shanti.

Baloo was also confused. "But you . . . you told me to scarify her!" he said to Mowgli.

"Wait a minute," Shanti said to Mowgli. "You planned this?"

Thinking it was another one of Mowgli's tricks, Shanti grabbed Ranjan and rushed off.

Mowgli caught up with Shanti and Ranjan. But before he could explain, Shere Khan appeared.

"You seem surprised to see me," said Shere Khan.

"Run," Mowgli whispered to Shanti.

Tossing dirt into the tiger's eyes, Mowgli ran, too.

Shere Khan chased the children through the tall jungle grass. Mowgli knew they couldn't outrun the powerful tiger.

"Come on! This way!" he shouted to his friends. Mowgli found a safe hiding place for Shanti and Ranjan. Then he ran to some ancient ruins, leading Shere Khan away from his friends.

Shanti told Ranjan to stay put and hurried off to help Mowgli. But little Ranjan wanted to help, too. He raced out and ran right into Baloo.

"Whoa, calm down kid," said Baloo. "Now where's Mowgli?"

"Shere Khan!" was all Ranjan could say.

Baloo tucked little Ranjan onto his shoulders and rushed to rescue his pal.

Meeting up with Bagheera, Baloo told the panther to watch Ranjan. At the ruins, Baloo bumped into Shanti! The two realized that they were both trying to help Mowgli.

Then they saw Mowgli hiding as Shere Khan prowled nearby.

"No matter how fast you run. No matter where you hide. I will catch you!" the tiger growled as he searched for Mowgli.

Shanti and Baloo quickly came up with a plan.

Baloo banged on a gong to distract Shere Khan. The sound echoed through the ruins. Then Shanti banged on one. Mowgli got the idea and banged on his gong.

The tiger was confused. The plan was working until Shanti's gong fell over!

To keep Shere Khan from hurting Shanti, Mowgli stepped between them.

Mowgli and Shanti ran up a set of stairs. Then they jumped from a ledge onto a giant stone tiger-head perched high above a fiery pit.

Shere Khan jumped after them. But the stone tiger-head began to crumble under Shere Khan's weight.

Just as they were all about to fall into the fiery pit, Baloo grabbed onto Shanti and Mowgli.

But Shere Khan tumbled and landed on a rock. Seconds later the stone tiger-head fell, trapping him inside.

The three triumphant friends happily met up with Bagheera and Ranjan, who were very glad to see them.

In the distance, they heard the villagers shouting for them. The time had finally come. Although Mowgli would always love the jungle, he knew that the village was his home now. Sadly, he said good-bye to his jungle friends.

When the children were reunited with the other villagers, everyone was very relieved and happy.

Even Mowgli was happy. Somehow, he knew he would see his jungle friends again very soon. . . .

EYE SPY

For a swinging good time, head back into the jungle and try to find these cool pictures.

Dear Parents:

You probably know or have known a child with Asperger's syndrome. *Understanding Sam* will help you understand Asperger's syndrome and thereby recognize that such children are heroes.

Tony Attwood, Ph.D., author,
The Complete Guide to Asperger's Syndrome

Skeezel Press
2624 Lakeside Drive, Erie, PA 16511 USA

Publisher's Cataloging-in-Publication
Niekerk, Clarabelle van.
Understanding Sam and Asperger syndrome / story by Clarabelle van Niekerk & Liezl Venter; pictures by Clarabelle van Niekerk.
p. cm.
SUMMARY: A young boy named Sam, has difficulty at school and seems moody at home. When Sam is diagnosed with a form of autism called Asperger syndrome, his family and teachers understand him better and learn how to help him succeed. Includes tips for parents, teachers and children on being with children who have Asperger's.
Audience: Ages 4-8.
LCCN 2007939834
ISBN-13: 978-0-9747217-1-2
ISBN-10: 0-9747217-1-9
1. Asperger's syndrome--Juvenile literature.
[1. Asperger's syndrome. 2. Autism.] I. Venter, Liezl.
II. Title.
RC553.A88N54 2008 616.85'8832 QBI07-600292

ISBN: 978-0-9747217-1-2
Printed in China Set in PrioriSan and Submarine

Book design by Tungsten Creative Group
Illustrations photographed by Rob Ruby Photography